Believe Me, GOLDILOCKS ROCKS!

The story of THE THREE BEARS as told by BABY BEAR

by Nancy Loewen   illustrated by Tatevik Avakyan

Raintree

www.raintreepublishers.co.uk
Visit our website to find out
more information about
Raintree books.

To order:
☏ Phone 0845 6044371
🖹 Fax +44 (0) 1865 312263
✉ Email myorders@raintreepublishers.co.uk

Customers from outside the UK please telephone +44 1865 312262

Raintree is an imprint of Capstone Global Library
Limited, a company incorporated in England and Wales
having its registered office at 7 Pilgrim Street, London,
EC4V 6LB – Registered company number: 6695582

We would like to thank Terry Flaherty, Professor of
English at Minnesota State University, for his advice
and expertise.

Editors: Jill Kalz and Vaarunika Dharmapala
Designer: Lori Bye
Art Director: Nathan Gassman
Production Specialist: Sarah Bennett
The illustrations in this book were created digitally.

ISBN 978 1 406 24309 3 (paperback)
16 15 14 13 12
10 9 8 7 6 5 4 3 2 1

**British Library Cataloguing in
Publication Data**
A full catalogue record for this book is
available from the British Library.

First things first: my name is NOT Baby Bear. It's Sam. Secondly, I am not nearly as wee or small or tiny as people think.

As for Goldilocks, ever since she broke into my house, she's been one of my best friends. It's true that she takes a lot of chances. Even so, she's a good sort – at least, she's no worse than me. Let me tell you the REAL story, and you'll see.

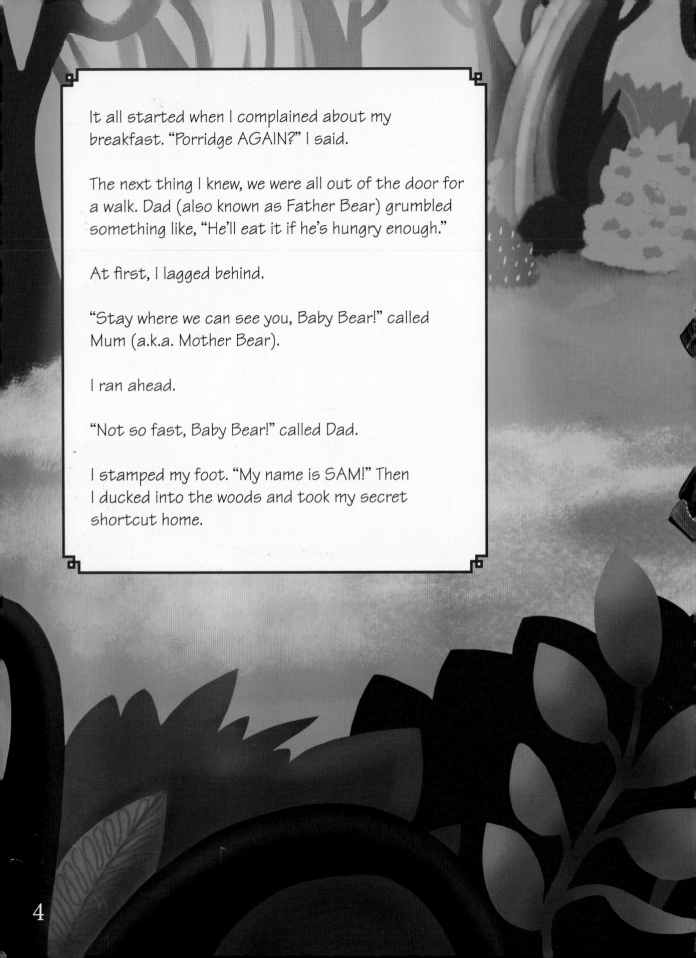

It all started when I complained about my breakfast. "Porridge AGAIN?" I said.

The next thing I knew, we were all out of the door for a walk. Dad (also known as Father Bear) grumbled something like, "He'll eat it if he's hungry enough."

At first, I lagged behind.

"Stay where we can see you, Baby Bear!" called Mum (a.k.a. Mother Bear).

I ran ahead.

"Not so fast, Baby Bear!" called Dad.

I stamped my foot. "My name is SAM!" Then I ducked into the woods and took my secret shortcut home.

When I reached our house, I heard a voice. Someone was inside!

I didn't know what to do. Should I run to Mum and Dad for help? Or should I chase off the intruder myself?

"Baby Bear" would have made a run for it. Not Sam, though.

I peeked through the kitchen window. A girl was taking pictures with her mobile phone!

"Ha! This will teach Little Red Riding Hood to double-dare me," she muttered. "Goldilocks does not lose at Truth or Dare!"

She paused in front of the porridge bowls. "Eeeeeww," she said.

I liked her already.

Goldilocks took a picture of herself in Dad's chair ...

... then in Mum's chair.

"You want proof, Little Miss Hoodie?" she said. "Here it is!"

Next, she took a picture of herself in my chair. When she tried to get up, the chair stuck to her bottom. She waddled around. She jumped up and down. Finally, she gave the chair a good whack and it came off in pieces.

"Oops," she said. "There goes my pocket money."

See? She meant to pay us back. Not that I cared. That chair was way too small for me, too.

9

Upstairs, Goldilocks slipped off her shoes (which was very thoughtful of her) and took a video of herself jumping on Mum and Dad's beds.

"I can't believe I'm doing this!" she giggled.

Now, jumping on the beds is NOT ALLOWED in my house. This was my one and only chance to get away with it. I tapped at the window.

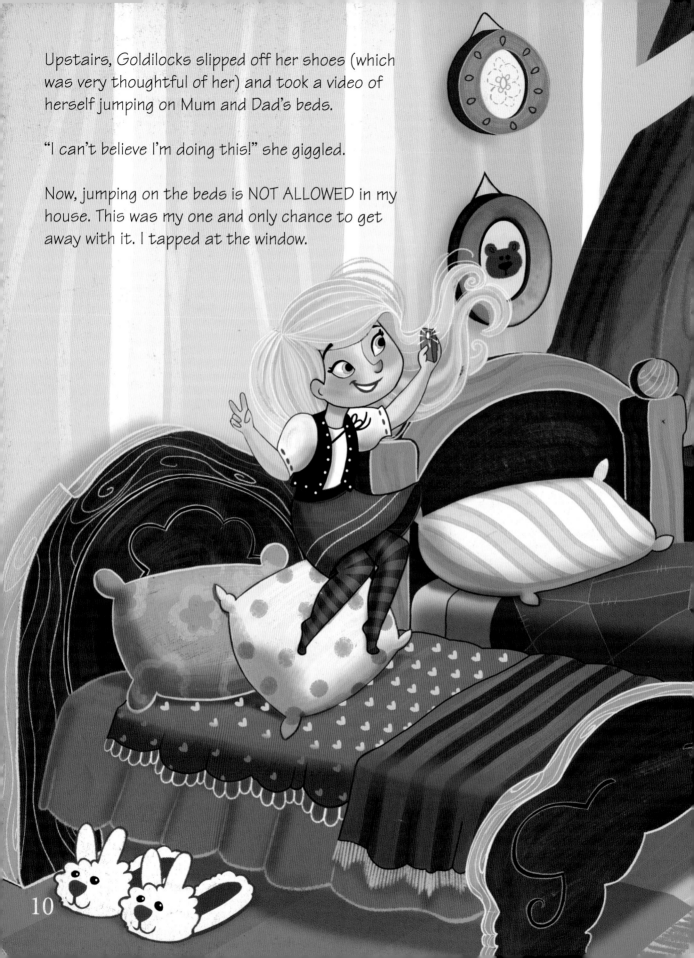

"EEK!"

Goldilocks shrieked.

"Let me in!" I begged. "I won't tell!"

Goldilocks opened the window, and we introduced ourselves. She apologized for breaking in. We were really quite civilized.

11

Then we **jumped** and **jumped** and **jumped** and **jumped** ...

... until we heard my mum calling from the woods. "Ba-by Bearrrr, where arrrre you?"

Goldilocks raised an eyebrow. "Baby Bear?" she asked. "Seriously?"

"Never mind that!" I said. "I have a plan ..."

13

I ran downstairs just as my parents were coming in.

"Baby Bear!" Mum exclaimed. "Thank goodness you're all right."

"There's an intruder upstairs!" I said.

"You know better than to go around making up stories," Dad said.

They sat down to eat their porridge – their cold, dried-out porridge.

I brought in my broken chair. "See? The intruder did this!"

"What a naughty thing to do!" Dad said. "Wrecking a perfectly good chair just to get our attention."

"But I SAW her!" I insisted. "Come on!"

I tugged them upstairs and showed them the messy covers on their beds.

"Baby Bear, you know that jumping on the beds is a big no-no!" Mum scolded.

"But the intruder —" I said, pushing them towards my room.

As soon as we reached my bed ...

"BOO!"

Goldilocks yelled.

What happened next was priceless.

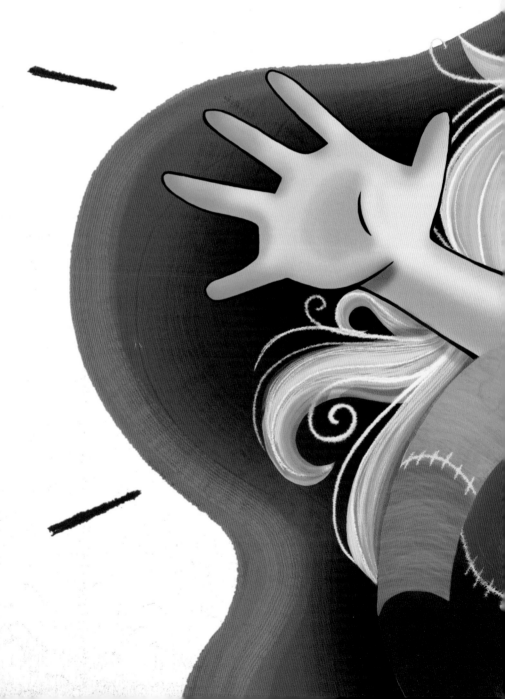

"Run!" Dad cried.

"To our safe place!" Mum screeched.
"If we don't make it – I love you both with all my heart!"

I made sure they saw me chasing Goldilocks through the woods. In between her fake screams and my pretend growls, we swapped mobile numbers.

Mum and Dad were so impressed with my courage they gave me everything I asked for: a bigger chair, flapjacks for breakfast instead of porridge, and a promise to stop calling me Baby Bear.

Well, there was one thing I didn't get.

"Can't I jump on the beds? Just once in a while?" I asked.

"NO," my parents said. "ABSOLUTELY NOT."

Oh well, it was worth a try.

Think about it

Read a classic version of *Goldilocks and the Three Bears* and compare it to Sam's version. What are some things that happen in this story that do not happen in the classic? What are some things that happen in the classic story that do not appear in this one?

Most versions of *Goldilocks and the Three Bears* are told from an invisible narrator's point of view. This version is told from Baby Bear's point of view. Which point of view do you think is true? Why?

How do you think this story would be different if it was told from another character's point of view? What if Mother Bear told the story? Father Bear? Goldilocks?

Sam does not think that Goldilocks was a bad person, even though she broke into his house. Do you agree or disagree? Why?

What do you think would have happened if Sam had run back to his parents instead of seeing what Goldilocks was up to?

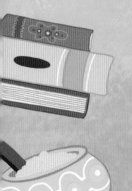

⊰ ❖❖❖ ⊱

Glossary

character person, animal, or creature in a story
narrator person who tells a story
point of view way of looking at something
version account of something from a certain
   point of view

Books in this series:

Believe Me, GOLDILOCKS ROCKS!

The story of THE **THREE BEARS** as told by **BABY BEAR**

by Nancy Loewen   illustrated by Tatevik Avakyan

978 1 406 24309 3

Honestly, RED RIDING HOOD WAS ROTTEN!

The story of LITTLE **RED RIDING HOOD** as told by **THE WOLF**

by Trisha Shaskan   illustrated by Gerald Guerlais

978 1 406 24310 9

Seriously, CINDERELLA IS SO ANNOYING!

The story of **CINDERELLA** as told by **THE WICKED STEPMOTHER**

by Trisha Shaskan   illustrated by Gerald Guerlais

978 1 406 24311 6

Trust Me, JACK'S BEANSTALK STINKS!

The story of **JACK AND THE BEANSTALK** as told by **THE GIANT**

by Eric Braun   illustrated by Cristian Bernardini

978 1 406 24312 3

24